JOSEPH COELHO

ALL POEMS ALOUD

THIS BOOK BELONGS TO:

I celebrated World Book Day® 2025 with this gift
from my local bookseller and Wide Eyed Editions

WORLD BOOK DAY®

World Book Day's mission is to offer every child and young person the opportunity
to read and love books by giving you the chance to have a book of your own.
To find out more, and for fun activities including video stories, audiobooks and
book recommendations, visit worldbookday.com
World Book Day® is a charity sponsored by National Book Tokens.

WIDE EYED EDITIONS

FSC
www.fsc.org
MIX
Paper | Supporting
responsible forestry
FSC® C118234

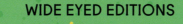

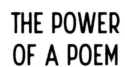

THE POWER OF A POEM

People sometimes are a bit scared of poetry... that's because it's very powerful! Why not try performing this poem with some friends? Divide the lines up between you, read some lines separately, read some together. Maybe you can get the audience to join in on the repeating lines.

A poem has the power
to build the highest tower,
to paint the prettiest flower!
A poem has the power.

In that tower of flowers
you may find a blooming power
as you paint with pollen and petal
you'll find a rose can test your mettle.

A poem has the skill
to cure any ill,
turn thoughts to windmills!
A poem has the skill.

As new ideas spin
the problems they're curing,
will waft away with time
all because of a little rhyme.

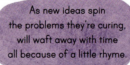

A poem has the capability
to conquer all hostility
to play a song of tranquillity!
A poem has the capability.

Words can hurt and soothe
but you'll make the spiky smooth,
apply a sentence like a balm
use a poem to heal and calm.

A poem has the might,
to give your passion bite,
to let your words take flight!
A poem has the might.

Your words might change a mind,
inspire someone to be kind,
or your words might roar
with the bite of a dinosaur.

4

RIDDLES

These tricky riddles put your audience to the test. Will they work out the answer from your clues? Speak slowly and carefully and repeat your riddle if necessary.

BEHIND YOU

I'm always behind you
very rarely in front
except when I go travelling.
I eat your lunch before you do.
I've seen all your books.
Whatever you give me
I'll make sure no one else will take a look.

BELOW YOU

I often stink,
but have a soul (sort of)
I keep you knotted
so you never trip.
When you run
I help you get a grip.

NEAR YOU

I'm clear when I'm empty,
see-through when I'm full.
My insides taste of nothing,
yet you want me.
Need me!
I'm full of leaks and gulps.
My brothers choke the oceans.

*Backpack **Trainer ***Water Bottle

CLUB RULES

Here are the rules to join Werewolf Club. Can you make up the rules for other monster clubs? What are the rules for Zombie Club? Everyone must eat brains? What are the rules for Loch Ness Club? No photos allowed? What are the rules for Witch Club? Be sure to know which witch is which.

MEAT NOT SWEETS

NO CATS

WW ONLY

DO NOT ENTER!

N
CH
TO

7

WEREWOLF CLUB RULES

Do not talk about Werewolf Club!
You can howl about it,
but never talk!

Do not walk to Werewolf Club!
You can bound to it in moonlight,
but never walk!

Do not eat sweets at Werewolf Club!
You can eat meat, raw meat,
but no sweets!

Do not bring cats to Werewolf Club!
You can bring bats, hats and even rats,
but no cats!

Do not bring silver to Werewolf Club!
You can bring gold or pewter or even bronze,
but no silver!

Do not bring chewy toys to Werewolf Club!

If you do they will be confiscated.

You won't get them back.

They are very squeaky
and make it hard
for us to hear the day's agenda!

POEMS TO WHISPER

When you are performing, your audience can be lots of people, or just one.
Try whispering these poems in a friend's ear.

TICKLE BREATH

My breath in your ear may delight and tickle
may make you squirm, and laugh and wiggle
as I get uncomfortably near.

But I have something lovely to say
a little thought to brighten your day.
Your smile makes everyone cheer.

DON'T LOOK NOW

Don't look now
don't move, don't breathe
there's something behind you
unlike anything I've seen
it's looking
right at you
eyes hollow as night
it's pointing its long fingers.
Its mouth wants to bite.
It's moving its grey lips
so horribly slow
the words it is saying
are whispered and low.
Don't look now
it's incredibly near
don't move a hair's width,
It's whispering in your ear.

POEMS THAT SHOUT

Each word in a poem is special and meaningful. That is why if you have an important message to tell, a poem is a good way to get it across loud and clear.

FROM SPACE

Seen from space
our planet is
a blue marble,
tiny and vulnerable,
a child's plaything.

When giants play at marbles
the marbles often crack.
A crack for all the plastic
clogging up the seas.
A crack for all the pollution,
a crack for the felling of trees.
A crack for all the oil
that spills and coats and chokes,
a crack for every politician
who says global warming's a joke.

Seen from space
our planet is
a teary eye,
sad and soft,
begging to be wiped.
When tears are left to pool

sadness drowns us all...
A tear for the crops
that can no longer flourish and grow.
A tear for every child
who will never get to grow old.
A tear for every bullet,
every bomb
that should have never been made.
A tear for the next generation
who never asked to play this game.

Given a little space,
could the planet heal?

Space for the fish
to repopulate the seas.
Space for the forests
to once again know trees.
Space for the skies to cry away the
smoke.
Space for the next generation
to fix what their forefathers broke.

SAYING NO

It's great to try new things but sometimes we don't feel like doing something, and that's ok too. This poem uses a lot of rhyme. Can you write a rhyming poem about being asked to do lots of very silly things? Like putting jelly in your wellies! Or planting your socks! I'm guessing your answer would be to say "no"!

I would say "yes"
all the time.
"Yes" to this, "yes" to that.
I had a multitude of "yeses"
underneath my hat.

"Yes" to every question,
"yes" to things I did not want to do.
I had "yeses" in my pockets
and found "yeses" in my shoes.

"Yes" when I was tired,
"yes" when I was sad.
I would say "yes" to everything
even when "yes" made me feel bad.

"Yes" I can help you with your jacket,
"Yes" I can help you carry those.
But what is this beneath my feet?
A pile of little "nos".

"No" I don't want to go there,
"no" I don't want to play that,
"no" I don't feel like doing that thing
and that's the end of that.

I started to say "no",
never to be cruel or mean,
just when I didn't want to,
when I wasn't feeling keen.

Then a funny thing happened
when I decided to say "yes".
I said "yes" because I wanted to
and "yes" felt like the best.

I said "yes" and felt so happy,
I said "yes" and felt so strong.
I said "no" to playing football,
but said "yes" to singing a song.

I said "no thanks" to a hug
but "yes please" to a fist bump.
I said "sorry... no"
when asked if my skateboard
could be used for a skidding jump.

Now my pockets are full of "yeses"
but also quite a few "nos"!
I pick and choose between the two,
"yes" to these, but "no" to those.

"Yes" when I want to
or feel it's only fair.
"No" when I don't want to,
when there's something else
I'd rather dare...

Something else I want to try,
another thing I want to do.
So often a "no" to one thing
is a "yes" to something new.

FUN WITH ANIMAL NAMES

Try playing with the endings of some different animal names –
crocodile, octopus, platypus, rhinoceros, scorpion and orangutan –
and putting them in your own poem. When a platypus has a cold,
does it sneeze-ypus? Have fun and remember to smile-odile like a crocodile!

HIPPOPOT-AMUS

I know a hippopotamus
he sips from a teapot-amus
he's such a proper hippopotamus
he ties his tie with a Windsor knot-amus.

I know a hippopotamus
who won the jackpot-amus
and sails on his yacht-amus
such a lucky hippopotamus.

ARMADILL-O

I met an armadillo
who could never chill-o
spent her day on the treadmill-o
such a sporty armadillo.

I met an armadillo
who ran from here to Brazil-o
uphill and downhill-o
purely for the thrill-o.

I met an armadillo
a very tired armadillo
not moving, totally still-o
fast asleep on her pillow.

AYE-AYE

I once saw an aye-aye
such a creepy little aye-aye
staring at me with her eye-eye.
I left with a quick bye-bye.

Around every corner there's that aye-aye
she's following me, but why-why?
such a creepy little aye-aye
I wonder if she's a spy-spy?

I run around town as I try-try
to lose this private eye-eye
but wherever I go she's nearby-by
that creepy little aye-aye.

TONGUE TWISTERS

are a wonderful way to improve your diction
(how clearly you can say words). Make sure
every word is powerful and is heard.

TRY

Try twisting your tongue
then tuning your teeth,
try taking your tonsils
from a tummy tickling thief.

Try tasting your tears
then trumpeting your toes,
try taping your temper
to the tip of your nose.

A WITCHY NIGHT

Witchy fingers.
Witchy toes.
Witchy wart.
Witchy nose.
Witchy hat
upon your head.
Witchy dreams
in a witchy bed!

Witchy wakes
on a witchy night.
Witchy cat on a broom.
Witchy cauldron.
Witchy spoon.
Witchy shoes
on your feet.
Witchy spells.
Wow!
Witchy treats.

Witchy laugh
all cackle cackle.
Witchy mog –
raised hackles.
Witchy dance
on a witchy night.
Witchy party.
Witchy fright.

Witches here and witches there
witches soaring through the air.
Witches conjuring all sorts of riches,
collecting frogs from muddy ditches.

Witches together on All Hallows' Eve –
a ball like you would not believe.

DISCOVER MORE POETRY BOOKS FROM JOSEPH COELHO

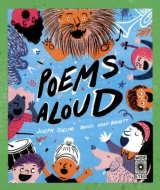

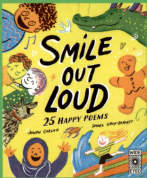

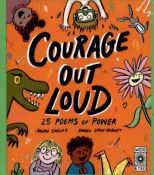

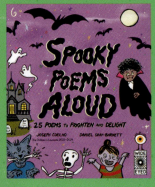

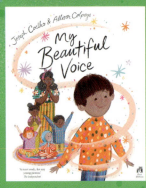

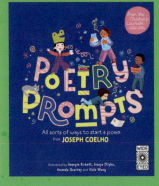

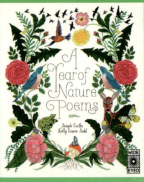